Bounder to the Rescue

Published in the UK by Scholastic Education, 2022
Scholastic Distribution Centre, Bosworth Avenue, Tournament Fields, Warwick, CV34 6UQ
Scholastic Ireland, 89E Lagan Road, Dublin Industrial Estate, Glasnevin, Dublin, D11 HP5F

SCHOLASTIC and associated logos are trademarks and/or registered trademarks of Scholastic Inc.
www.scholastic.co.uk
© 2022 Scholastic
1 2 3 4 5 6 7 8 9   2 3 4 5 6 7 8 9 0 1

Printed by Ashford Colour Press
The book is made of materials from well-managed, FSC®-certified forests and other controlled sources.

A CIP catalogue record for this book is available from the British Library.

ISBN 978-0702-30910-6

All rights reserved. This book is sold subject to the condition that it shall not, by way of trade or otherwise, be lent, hired out or otherwise circulated in any form of binding or cover other than that in which it is published. No part of this publication may be reproduced, stored in a retrieval system, or transmitted in any form or by any other means (electronic, mechanical, photocopying, recording or otherwise) without prior written permission of Scholastic Limited.

Every effort has been made to trace copyright holders for the works reproduced in this publication, and the publishers apologise for any inadvertent omissions.

Author
Catherine Baker
Editorial team
Rachel Morgan, Vicki Yates, Fiona Undrill, Jennie Clifford
Design team
Dipa Mistry, Justin Hoffmann, Andrea Lewis, We Are Grace
Illustrations
Anna Mazepa/Beehive illustration

Can you spot the rabbit on 10 pages?

Help your child to read!

This book practises these letters and letter sounds.
Point and say the sounds with your child:

- ay (as in 'day')
- ou (as in 'out')
- ea (as in 'sea')
- ir (as in 'girl')
- ue (as in 'blue')
- u (as in 'unicorn')

Your child may need help to read these common tricky words:

- was, we, to, the, my, sure, he, when, I, me, said
- likes, some, of, she, all, push, pulled, into, you

Before reading
- Look at the cover picture and read the title together. Read the back cover blurb to your child.
- Ask your child: *Where do you think this story is set? Who is Bounder? How do you think a dog like Bounder might rescue someone?*

During reading
- If your child gets stuck on a word, remind them to sound it out and then blend the sounds to read the word: T-ue-s-d-ay, Tuesday.
- If they are still stuck, show them how to read the word.
- Enjoy looking at the pictures together. Pause to talk about the story.

After reading
- Ask your child: *Can you remember how Bounder rescued Fay?*
- *Can you think of three good words to describe Bounder?*

Tuesday was a hot day. We went to the beach for a picnic.

It was my dog Bounder's first trip to the sea.

At first, Bounder was not sure about the sea.

But when I went for a swim, Bounder joined me.
He splashed about at first.
Then he started to swim too.

"Look!" said Dad. "Bounder likes the sea!"

Bounder, Dad and I swam a long way.

Then we had a picnic lunch.
Bounder had some of my pie!

I spotted a girl playing in the sea.
Her toy was sitting on a blue plastic unicorn.

At first, the sea wasn't deep.

But it got deeper, and the unicorn drifted a long way out from the beach.

She shouted for help.

Her dad ran along the beach.
"Help me rescue Fay's toy!" he shouted.
"I cannot swim!"

We all jumped up.
Bounder reached the sea first.

Bounder swam out to the blue unicorn. He tried to push it back to the beach, but it kept floating away.

Then he grabbed the unicorn's string in his mouth.

Fay's dad splashed into the sea to help get the unicorn.

"Thank you!" cried Fay's dad.
"Good boy, Bounder!" I said.

Bounder the rescuer wagged his tail.

Retell the story